**Project 7-11**

# Moving on in Reading and Writing

## Book 2

Sheila Lane and Marion Kemp

for 9-10 year olds

Letts

# 1 What kind of person are you?

Did you know . . .
that there were **Sin-Eaters** in parts of Herefordshire long ago?

▶ Read the old notice on the church door.

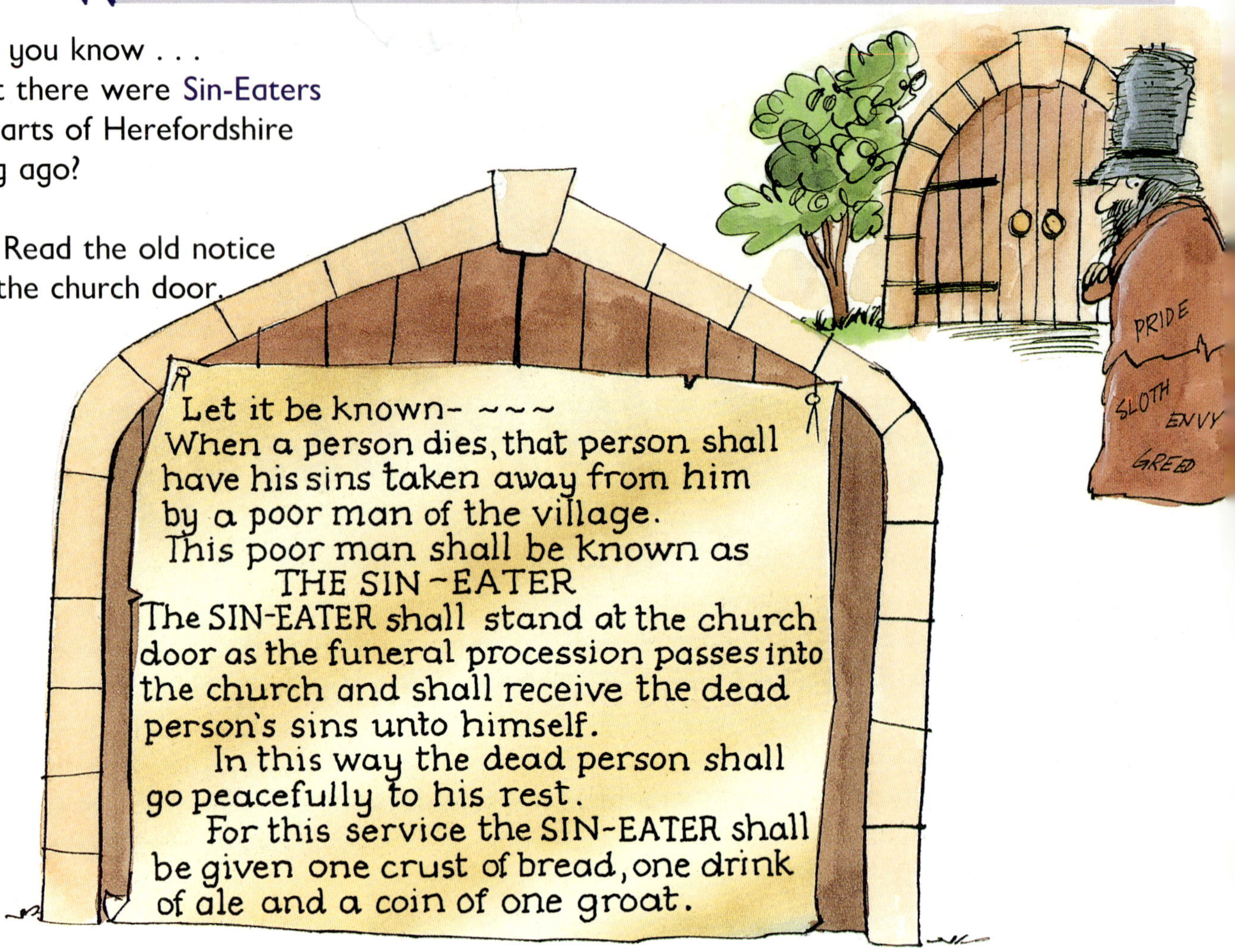

Let it be known- ~~~
When a person dies, that person shall have his sins taken away from him by a poor man of the village.
This poor man shall be known as
THE SIN-EATER
The SIN-EATER shall stand at the church door as the funeral procession passes into the church and shall receive the dead person's sins unto himself.
In this way the dead person shall go peacefully to his rest.
For this service the SIN-EATER shall be given one crust of bread, one drink of ale and a coin of one groat.

*I don't think anyone's sins can be given to someone else.*

What do you think?
▶ Write here.
*I do not think the sins can*

*I don't think the Sin-Eater was paid enough for what he did.*

What do you think?
▶ Write here.
*I don't think so*

*I wonder what some of the sins were?*

▶ Write some sins in the Sin-Eater's hat.

*greediness
selfishness
lazyness
fighting
lying
killing*

**Do you have any faults?**

*In the Sin-Eater's hat:*
- grumbling ✓
- bad temper ✓
- selfishness ✓
- foolishness ✓
- pencil chewing
- untidiness ✓
- being late
- nail biting ✓
- greediness

*A fault is ... a mistake ... or a failing ... or a slip ... or a weakness.*

Do you ever make mistakes?
Do you have any bad habits?
Are you sometimes slow to do things?
Do you sometimes feel cross ...
or angry ... or bad-tempered?

▶ Tick the **faults** in the Sin-Eater's hat which might be **yours**.
Which do you think is your **worst** fault?
▶ Write it here.

_Arguing_

Have you ever tried to 'Turn over a new leaf'?

*To 'turn over a new leaf' means to 'have a fresh start and do better'.*

▶ In the 'New Leaf' of the notebook, write the **opposites** of some of the faults in the Sin-Eater's hat.

*Notebook page 1:*
good temper
bieng early
tidyness
unselfish
unfolish

Some words are given an **opposite** meaning by putting **un-** in front of them.

**LOOK!**

| forgiving | kind | sure | fair |
| **un**forgiving | **un**kind | **un**sure | **un**fair |

▶ Make **opposites** by writing **un-** in front of the following words.

_un_ selfish   _un_ happy   _un_ true   _un_ wise   _un_ tidy   _un_ safe

_un_ willing   _un_ healthy   _un_ clean   _un_ pleasant   _un_ popular

Write more nouns which mean: **fault** in your Thesaurus on pages 38–39.

Fill in your book file.

**Book file**
★ Fair
★★ Good
★★★ Excellent

# 2 What do you say?

Super! Fabulous! Fantastic!

Do all these words mean **excellent**?

superb         outstanding
       sly
marvellous       terrific
     first class

▶ Write the 'odd one out'.

_Sly_

▶ Fill in the missing words in the balloon.

_Sly_ is the odd one out because it means _cunning_.

Crazy! Daft! Stupid!

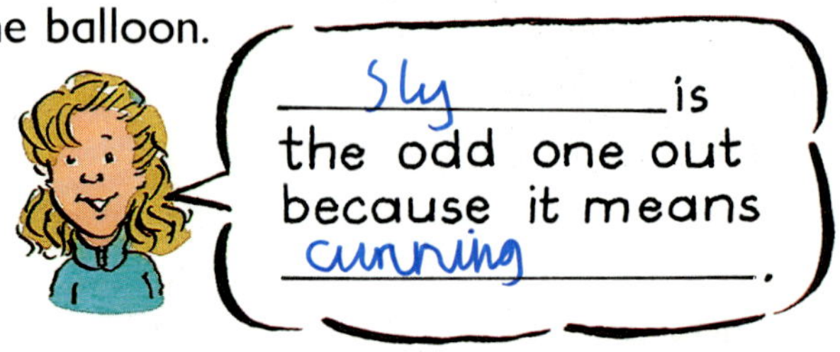

Do all these words mean **ridiculous**?

silly     foolish     laughable
  absurd       senseless
     sensible

▶ Write the 'odd one out'.

_Sensible_

▶ Fill in the missing words in the balloon.

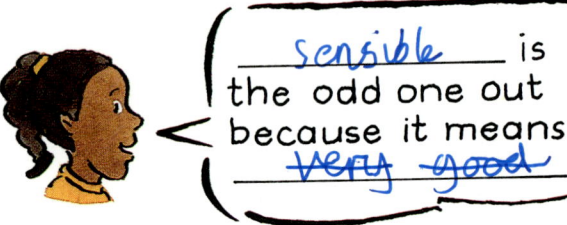

_Sensible_ is the odd one out because it means ~~very good~~.

_Having common sense_

▶ Draw a ring round the words which have **similar** meanings to the word in **capital letters**.

HAPPY    (glad) sorry (delighted) (contented) (cheerful)

ANGRY    (cross) (mad) (furious) cheerful vexed

BRILLIANT   (dazzling) nice (gleaming) (glittering) (shining)

COLD    warm (freezing) (chilly) (frozen) (icy)

BAD    (wicked) (rotten) usual (evil) (sinful)

ASTONISHED   (amazed) surprised (astounded) expected

Write more adjectives which mean:
(a) **excellent** and (b) **ridiculous**
in your Thesaurus on pages 38 – 39.

# Heads and tails

A **prefix** is an addition at the beginning of a word.

Some words are given **opposite** meanings by putting **dis-** in front of them.

▶ Make **opposites** by writing **dis-** in front of the following words.

_dis_ appear     _dis_ like     _dis_ obey

_dis_ grace     _dis_ honest     _dis_ pleased

_dis_ believe     _dis_ advantage     _dis_ agree

A **suffix** is an addition at the end of a word.
Some words are given **opposite** meanings by putting **-less** at the end of them.

▶ Make **opposites** by writing **-less** at the end of the following words.

care _less_     home _less_     use _less_

end _less_     fear _less_     power _less_

life _less_     breath _less_     noise _less_

▶ Write the clues for the puzzle by explaining the meaning of each answer word.

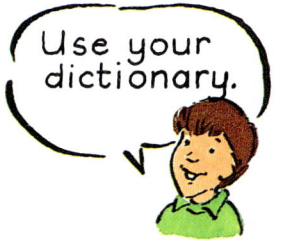

(Use your dictionary.)

▶ Read each answer in the puzzle.

| ¹d | i | s | a | p | p | e | a | r |
| ²d | i | s | o | b | e | y | | |
| ³d | i | s | h | o | n | e | s | t |
| ⁴d | i | s | l | i | k | e | | |
| ⁵d | i | s | a | g | r | e | e | |

1 To move out of sight.
2 not to obey
3 not honest
4 not to like someone or something
5 to have a different opinion

| ¹h | o | p | e | l | e | s | s |
| ²f | e | a | r | l | e | s | s |
| ³n | o | i | s | e | l | e | s | s |
| ⁴l | i | f | e | l | e | s | s |
| ⁵p | o | w | e | r | l | e | s | s |

1 without hope
2 without fear, brave
3 silent
4 DEAD
5 feeble.

# 3　The Chocolate Factory

▶ Read about Mr Willie Wonka.

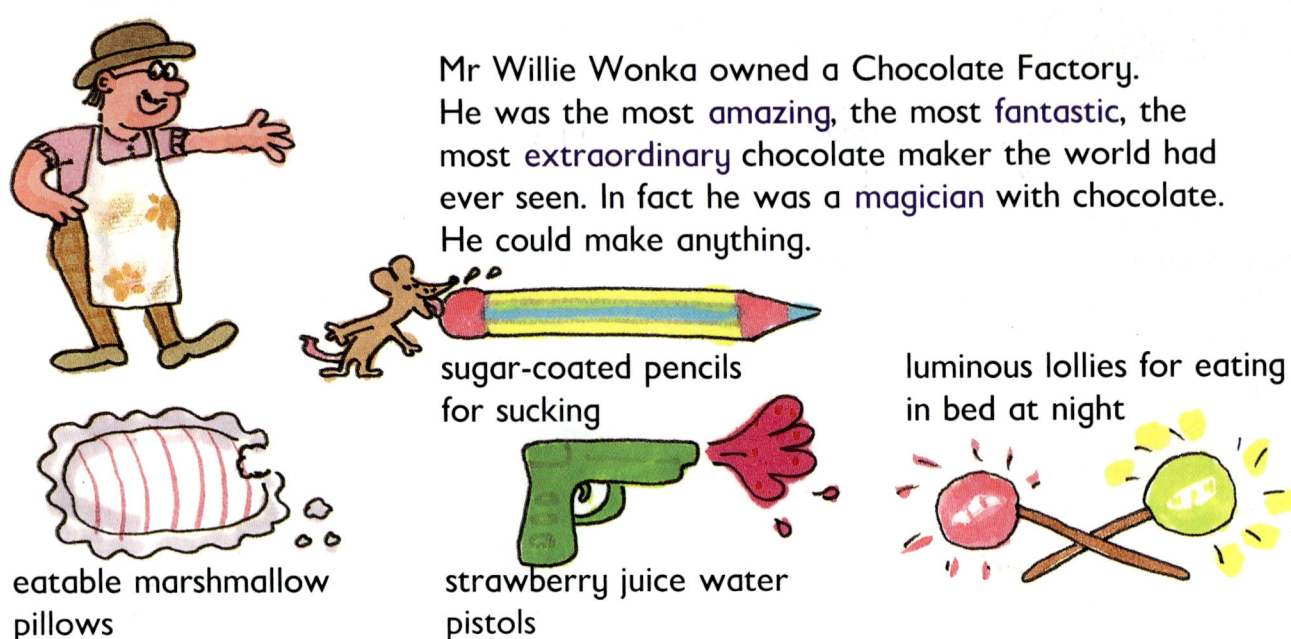

Mr Willie Wonka owned a Chocolate Factory. He was the most amazing, the most fantastic, the most extraordinary chocolate maker the world had ever seen. In fact he was a magician with chocolate. He could make anything.

sugar-coated pencils for sucking

luminous lollies for eating in bed at night

eatable marshmallow pillows

strawberry juice water pistols

▶ Invent three sweets of your own and give them names.

_____  _____  _____

Mr Willie Wonka invented a wonderful new chewing gum.

*This gum is my latest, my greatest, my most fascinating invention! This gum is a whole 3-course dinner all by itself.*

MENU
Tomato Soup
...
Roast Beef
...
Blueberry pie
....

Look what might happen if the gum machine went wrong.

▶ Write the menus correctly under each strip of gum.

| chocolate soup<br>chicken beef<br>roast pudding | lamb grapefruit<br>lemon chops<br>fresh tart | fish juice<br>rice fingers<br>tomato pudding |
|---|---|---|
| _____<br>_____<br>_____ | _____<br>_____<br>_____ | _____<br>_____<br>_____ |

▶ Read about Willie Wonka's Inventions Room.

*This is the most important room in the factory. So listen to me! No messing about when you go in. No touching, no meddling and no tasting.*

Inside the Inventions Room a monstrous gigantic machine
was spinning its wheels at breakneck speed.
The place was like a witch's kitchen...
black metal pots were boiling and bubbling...
kettles were hissing... pans were sizzling...
a strange iron machine was clanking and spluttering...
a small shiny machine was going phut-phut-phut...

▶ Describe the 3 different machines.

▶ Write here.

1 _____
2 _____
3 _____

▶ What sounds could be heard in the Inventions Room?

▶ Imagine the smells! What do you think some of them were?

Imagine... that one night, with Mr Willie Wonka's key in your hand, you make a secret visit to the Inventions Room.

Write a story about:
**My Night in the Chocolate Factory**

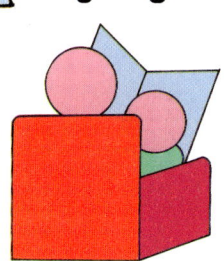

You could begin like this:

All the machines were still and silent. Seeing a winking red light above a gigantic lever, I...

Fill in your book file.

Book file
★ Fair
★★ Good
★★★ Excellent

# 4 Word pictures

▶ Read this description and make a picture in your mind of the Iron Man.

The Iron Man came to the top of the cliffs.

How far had he walked? Nobody knows. Where had he come from? Nobody knows. How was he made? Nobody knows.

Taller than a house, the Iron Man stood at the top of the cliff, on the very brink, in the darkness.

The wind sang through his iron fingers. His great iron head, shaped like a dustbin but as big as a bedroom, slowly turned to the right, slowly turned to the left. His iron ears turned, this way, that way. He was hearing the sea. His eyes, like headlamps, glowed white, then red, then infra-red, searching the sea. Never before had the Iron Man seen the sea.

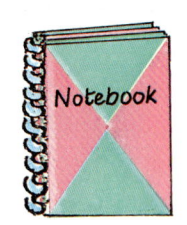

▶ Make a quick pencil sketch of the picture in your mind. Read the description again and **compare** the word picture with your sketch.

*When you compare two things, you decide what is the same about them.*

▶ 1   Complete this comparison.

The Iron Man was taller than _____

Write your own comparison for the Iron Man's great height.

He was taller than _____

▶ 2   Complete this comparison.

His great iron head was as big as _____

Write your own comparison for the Iron Man's head.

His head was as big as _____

▶ 3   Complete this comparison.

His eyes glowed like _____

Write your own comparison for the Iron Man's eyes.

His eyes glowed like _____

▶ Read this description.

Everything was there, old cars by the hundred, old trucks, old railway engines, old stoves, old refrigerators, old springs, bedsteads, bicycles, girders, gates, pans – all the scrap iron of the region was piled up there, rusting away.

The Iron Man gazed, and his eyes turned red. He picked up a greasy black stove and chewed it like toffee. There were delicious crumbs of chrome on it. He followed that with a double-decker bedstead and the brass knobs made his eyes crackle with joy. Never before had the Iron Man eaten such delicacies.

A big truck turned into the yard and unloaded a pile of rusty chain. The Iron Man lifted a handful and let it dangle into his mouth – better than any spaghetti. It was an Iron Man's heaven.

▶ Answer these questions.

1 What kind of food did the Iron Man enjoy most?

2 Where might a huge pile of this kind of food be found?

3 What might the Iron Man enjoy for a drink?

4 Where might he find a tasty drink?

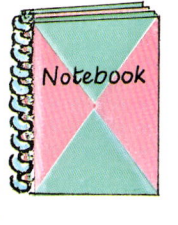

**Notebook**

Make a list of all the metal objects you can find **inside** and **outside** your home. Look out for tiny tit-bits like screws and nails. Think about how each would taste to the Iron Man. Write a word picture describing: **The Iron Man's Feast**

Have you read...?

The Iron Man by Ted Hughes

Write **yes** or **no**.

# 5  Give everything a name

*Have you got a... what's-it?*

*Lucy means a what-do-you-call-it...*

*or a... thingummyjig.*

*I'll look up what's-it in the dictionary... Ww...wa...we...wh...*

*Thingummyjig... Tt...ta...te...th...*

**Dictionary**
whale...
what... A word used in sentences to ask a question
wheat...

**Dictionary**
thin...
thing... Anything which can be seen or touched
think...

*No what's-it!*

*No thingummyjig!*

*So a what's-it or a thingummyjig could be just anything!*

▶ Read these verses about:

**Old Mrs Thing-um-e-bob**

Old Mrs Thing-um-e-bob,
　Lives at you-know-where,
Dropped her what-you-may-call-it down
　The well of the kitchen stair.

Along came Mr What's-his-name,
　He said, 'You've broken the lot!
I'll have to see what I can do
　With some of you-know-what.'
　　　　　　by Charles Causley

▶ Write your guess for the 'what-you-may-call-it'.

▶ Write your guess for the 'you-know-what'.

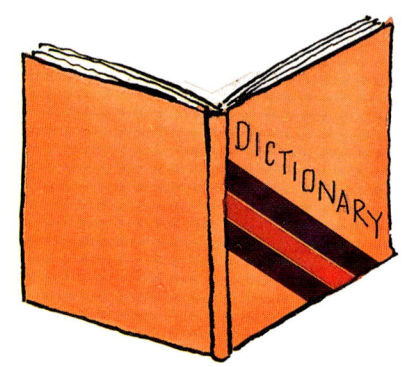

Do you have a real dictionary of your own? In dictionaries the words are arranged in alphabetical order.

**Remember!**

When more than one word in a set begins with the same letter, you need to look at the second letter.

▶ Arrange each set of words in alphabetical order.

1  exit _____
    ear _____
    even _____
    echo _____

2  mend _____
    map _____
    museum _____
    model _____

3  sense _____
    score _____
    spoon _____
    sting _____

Did you know that letter Q is <u>always</u> followed by letter U?

▶ Use a dictionary to help you write words beginning with **qu** which mean:

1  to make a noise like a duck _____
2  a woman who is a crowned ruler of a country _____
3  something which is asked _____     4  without sound _____
5  moving at speed _____     6  a large feather _____

▶ Use the clues and your dictionary to complete this **action words** puzzle.

to move with quick steps

to make a sound like a bell

to lift something up

to make short, sharp sounds

to put something back in its place

| r | | | | | |
| r | | | | | |
| r | | | | | |
| r | | | | | |
| r | | | | | |

Write more verbs which mean: to run and more nouns which mean: clue in your Thesaurus on pages 38 – 39.

# 6 Grammar

**1 ▶** Write the **names** of these people. Each name ends with **-er**.

1 someone who teaches <u>teacher</u>
2 someone who sells meat _____
3 someone who looks after a farm _____
4 someone who makes things out of wood _____
5 someone who sings _____

*A noun is a naming word.*

*An adjective is a describing word.*

*A verb is a word which tells you what is being done.*

**2 ▶** Draw a <u>line</u> under the **nouns** in these phrases.

1 a bright <u>**sun**</u>
2 a strong wind
3 a light breeze
4 a grey cloud
5 a thick fog
6 a violent storm

**3 ▶** Draw a ring round the **adjectives** in these phrases.

1 a **sunny** day
2 a windy corner
3 a breezy hill
4 a cloudy sky
5 a foggy night
6 a stormy voyage

*Did you notice that the adjectives in 3 were made from the nouns in 2?*

*Some adjectives are made by adding -y to a noun.*

**4 ▶** Write each **noun** and each **adjective** made from it.

1 <u>sun  sunny</u>
2 _____
3 _____
4 _____
5 _____
6 _____

**5 ▶** Write an **adjective** from each of these **nouns**.

1 mist <u>misty</u>
2 snow _____
3 rain _____
4 sand _____
5 crust _____
6 lump _____
7 flower _____
8 leaf _____
9 hill _____

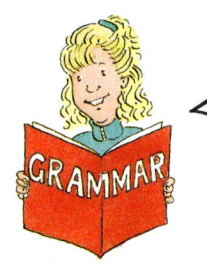

**Every sentence has a verb.**

▶ Write the missing **verbs** in this short piece from the story of **The Wizard of Oz**.

**The Search for the Wicked Witch of the West**

'We will _____ the Wicked Witch of the West,' _____ Dorothy,

'and we will _____ our journey early tomorrow morning.'

So the Tin Woodman _____ his axe, the Scarecrow _____

himself with fresh straw and the Cowardly Lion _____ his whiskers.

Then they all _____ to bed and _____ soundly until daylight.

Next morning a soldier _____ them through the streets of

Emerald City. He _____ the Great Green Gate.

'Which way is it to the Wicked Witch of the West?' _____ Dorothy.

'No one _____ that,' _____ the soldier.

**Nouns, adjectives and verbs are all parts of speech.**

**Think of them as sets or classes of things.**

▶ Colour in the **one** word in each **row** which tells you the name of the **part of speech** the other words belong to.

| sunny | misty | foggy | adjectives | rainy |
| butcher | nouns | soldier | baker | actor |
| laugh | cry | frown | smile | verbs |
| blue | yellow | crimson | brown | adjectives |
| talked | ran | went | verbs | knocked |
| beautiful | adjectives | ugly | soft | hard |

▶ Write more **verbs** which mean:
(a) to ask, (b) to begin and (c) to see
in your Thesaurus on pages 38–39.

# 1 The man-cub

▶ Read the beginning of chapter 1 of **The Jungle Book**. As you read, try to guess the missing words used by the author, Rudyard Kipling.

It was seven o'clock of a warm evening in the Seeone Hills when Father Wolf woke up from his day's rest, stretched himself, yawned and spread out his paws one after the other to get rid of the sleepy feeling in their tips.

   Mother Wolf lay with her big, __1__ nose dropped across her four, tumbling, squealing cubs and the moon shone into the mouth of the cave where they all lived.

   'Augrh!', said Father Wolf. 'It's time to hunt again.'

   Mother Wolf twitched one of her __2__. 'Wait,' she said, 'something is coming.'

   As the bushes which grew outside the __3__ parted a little, Father Wolf tensed his body. Then, just before he made his __4__ he saw what it was and tried to __5__ himself. The result was that he shot straight up into the air and landed where he had left the ground.

   'Mother Wolf,' he __6__. 'Look! It's a man-cub.'

▶ Read these clues for the missing words. Write your choice of word.

1 How could you describe Mother Wolf's nose ... gray ... black ... wet ... or ...?  _____

2 Which part of her body would Mother Wolf twitch?  _____

3 Where did the family live?  _____

4 Did Father Wolf bound ... or spring ... or ...?  _____

5 What was Father Wolf trying to do ... check ... or ...?  _____

6 What kind of sound did he make?  _____

Father and Mother Wolf took the little man-cub to the Council Rock. There, Akela, the leader of the Wolf Pack, held a meeting of all the wolves so that they could decide whether to keep the child.

"What harm can a naked cub do? Keep him, I say."

"Brothers! Will you take this man-cub into the Seeone Wolf Pack so that he can be one of us?"

"No! He's different from us... and the young ones will fight with him."

"To kill a small cub is a shame. Let him run with the Pack."

"Men and their cubs are wise. In time he may be able to help us all."

"Give the man-cub to Shere Khan, the tiger, for his meat."

"Men and their cubs are cunning. This cub will grow big and bring us trouble."

▶ In the picture above:
write a ✓ by the wolves who wanted to keep the man-cub;
write a ✗ by the wolves who were against keeping him.

Baloo, the brown bear, spoke for the man-cub.

"Let the man-cub run in the Pack with the other young ones. I, myself, will teach him all he needs to know to live among the jungle people."

Akela gave this warning.

"But can a man-cub be trained so that he can live among us and not die?"

▶ What will the man-cub have to learn if he is to live in the jungle?

_____
_____
_____
_____
_____

▶ How might the man-cub be able to help the wolves, when he is older?

_____
_____
_____
_____
_____

"Opinion means... view or belief."

Do **you** think the man-cub can be trained to live in the jungle?

▶ Give your opinion. _____
_____
_____

# 8 Life in the jungle

▶ Read more about the man-cub.

Mother Wolf called the man-cub Mowgli, which means, Little Frog. Baloo, the brown bear, became Mowgli's teacher and taught him The Laws of the Jungle.

> What must make no noise, Little Frog?

> Feet must make no noise, Baloo.

▶ Fill in the missing words in The Laws of the Jungle

_____ ... must make no noise,

_____ ... must see in the dark,

_____ ... must hear the wind in the night air,

_____ ... must be sharp and white.

▶ Read The Wood and Water Laws and write your choice of words.

So no Snake nor Bird nor Beast nor Water Creature shall hurt me, I must know the meaning of:

Every rustle of the _____ in the grass,

Every note of every _____ above my head,

Every scratch of a _____ claw,

Every splash of every little _____ moving in the waters.

Then I must learn:

How to speak politely to the wild _____ when I find their honey hidden in their hives.

What to say to the _____ when I disturb them in their day-time sleep.
How to warn the _____ in the pools, **before** I splash down among them.

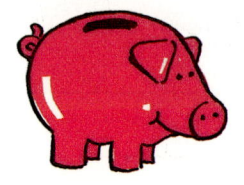

▶ Write more adjectives which mean:
(a) quiet, (b) noisy, (c) big and (d) small
in your Thesaurus on pages 38–39.

Mowgli, the man-cub, needed to use all his **five senses** of **sight**, **hearing**, **taste**, **touch** and **smell** for living in the Jungle.

In The Jungle Book it says:

> Now you must be content to skip ten or eleven whole years and only guess at all the wonderful life that Mowgli led among the wolves, because if it were written down it would fill ever so many books . . .

▶ Read these 5 story parts and write which of his five senses Mowgli used each time.

As Mowgli lay stretched out in the grass he suddenly saw the young calf's body go stiff with terror.

_____

Mowgli was creeping forward silently towards the safety of the den when the sharp snap of a twig a few yards ahead of him made him draw back.

_____

Mowgli put out a hand and touched the dark, red blood which lay in a warm, sticky pool in the hollow of the rock.

_____

The blue berries were quite different from those growing outside the den. Mowgli reached up his hand, squeezed one against his lips . . . it had a dry, bitter taste.

_____

Mowgli put up his head and sniffed the night air . . . This was a new scent . . . coming from the grey clouds which curled above the red flower . . .

_____

Use **one** of the ideas on this page. Write a story about: **Mowgli's Life in the Jungle**

Have you read . . .? *The Jungle Book* by Rudyard Kipling

Write **yes** or **no**.

# 9 Word play

## 1 Same letters – new word

▶ Fill in the puzzles by rearranging the letters of each word to make a new word.

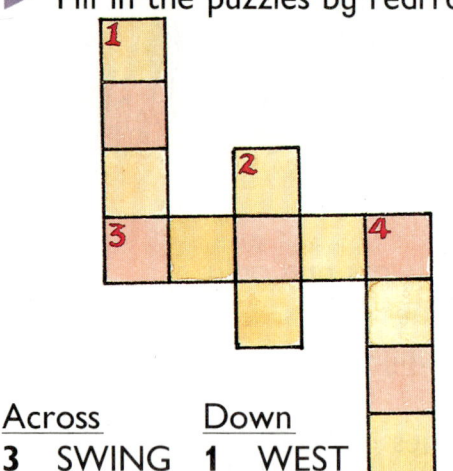

| Across | Down |
|---|---|
| 3 SWING | 1 WEST |
| | 2 TAN |
| | 4 EATS |

| Across | Down |
|---|---|
| 1 OWNS | 2 TEN |
| 3 TOP | 3 TIP |
| 4 NOTE | |

## 2 Crack the code

One way of hiding a message is to slide each letter **back** one place.

| z | a | b | c | d | e | f | g | h | i | j | k | l | m | n | o | p | q | r | s | t | u | v | w | x | y | z |
|---|---|---|---|---|---|---|---|---|---|---|---|---|---|---|---|---|---|---|---|---|---|---|---|---|---|---|
| a | b | c | d | e | f | g | h | i | j | k | l | m | n | o | p | q | r | s | t | u | v | w | x | y | z | a |

To say **on** you write **po**.

▶ Puzzle out this message:

dpnf  upebz  vshfou

To say **off** you write **pgg**.

▶ Write the message here.

_____  _____  _____

## 3 Hidden food and drink

▶ Find your way through 7 different foods and drinks. Start at  j  in the top left-hand corner and finish at  t  in the bottom left-hand corner. You can only move from one letter to the next by going up or down, left or right. The last letter of each word becomes the first letter of the next word.

▶ Write the names of the 7 foods and drinks here.

## 4 What is it?

▶ Use the clues and write the answers in the correct spaces in the crossword puzzle to find the answer to 'What is it?'

Across

1 A flat-bottomed glass
5 Bored a hole with a tool
7 The low sound that follows lightning

Down

2 Someone who uses something
3 A large, rounded container, filled with air or gas
4 A sudden attack
5 A hollow made in a flat surface
6 The border of something

Write the answer to 'What is it?' here. _____

## 5 What's the message?

▶ Number the words in each box 1–5 in alphabetical order. Then write the **second** letter of word number 1 under each box.

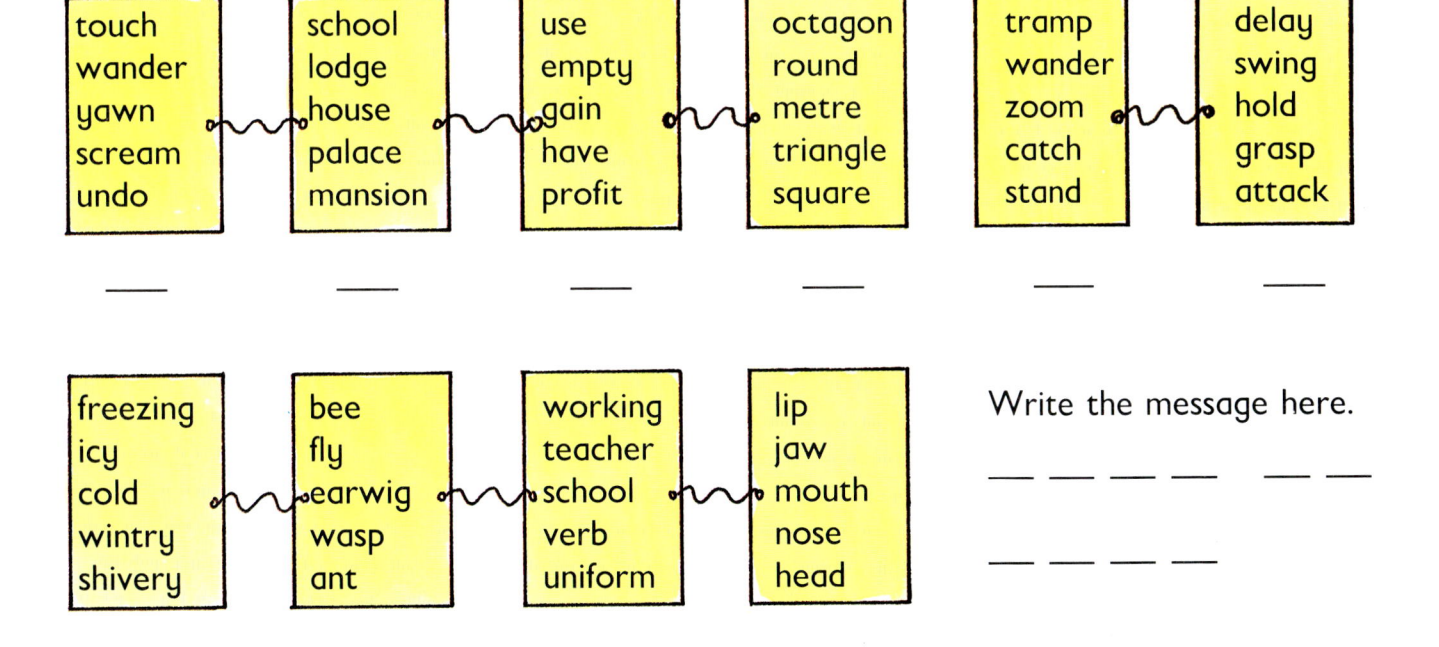

| touch | school | use | octagon | tramp | delay |
| wander | lodge | empty | round | wander | swing |
| yawn | house | gain | metre | zoom | hold |
| scream | palace | have | triangle | catch | grasp |
| undo | mansion | profit | square | stand | attack |

___   ___   ___   ___   ___   ___

| freezing | bee | working | lip |
| icy | fly | teacher | jaw |
| cold | earwig | school | mouth |
| wintry | wasp | verb | nose |
| shivery | ant | uniform | head |

___   ___   ___   ___

Write the message here.

___ ___ ___  ___ ___

___ ___ ___ ___

# 10 Writing with pictures

The boy in the picture goes to a hospital school each day in his wheel-chair.
He can't speak, or move his arms and legs, but he can see and hear.
He gives messages by pointing to pictures on his chart with the pointer on his helmet.

*A symbol is a sign which represents something.*

▶ Read this page of symbols from the chart.

| ⊥₁ = I or me | ↑ = up | ↓ = down |
| ⊥₂ = you | →⊥ = come |
| +‼ = yes | ✗→ = quick |
| −‼ = no | ♡∾ = pain |

Read these symbols for parts of the body.

| ⊥ = head | ∧ = leg |
| ⊙ = eye | ∧ᵥ = foot |
| ⊃ = ear | ⟨v⟩ = stomach |
| ᗯ = teeth | ✓ = hand |

▶ Write the symbols for:

| I or me ☐ | quick ☐ | teeth ☐ | foot ☐ |
| no ☐ | come ☐ | head ☐ | stomach ☐ |

| ♡ L = feeling | ♡ ↑↓ = feeling up and down = upset |
| ♡ ↑ = feeling up = happy | ♡ ↓? = feeling down…question = afraid |
| ♡ ↓ = feeling down = sad | ♡ ! = feeling…wow! = like  ♡ ‼! = feeling excited |

These symbols represent these words:
⊥₁ ♡∾ ᗯ = I pain tooth

The message is:
I have tooth-ache.

▶ Write the words and the message for each set of symbols.

1 ⊥₁ ♡∾ ⟨v⟩  _____

2 ⊥₂ →⊥ ✗→  _____

3 ⊥₁ ♡↑ ‼!  _____

▶ Make up a **Dictionary of Symbols** which you think might be useful to someone who needs to give messages with a pointer.

Here are two examples.

B ⋎ = <u>b</u>ird

C ⊓ = <u>c</u>hair

**Pictures** which represent **words** are called **pictograms**.
These pictograms can be seen in streets and roads.
▶ Write their meanings in **words**.

_____  _____
_____  _____
_____  _____

_____  _____
_____  _____
_____  _____

Today's weather

Pictograms are used for weather maps.
▶ Which part of the country would be:
(a) best for a picnic, _____
(b) a bad place for hanging
    out the washing to dry? _____

▶ Draw symbols for:
(a) snow            (b) thunder and lightning

You could make your own pictogram for each day for a month.

Have you read...?
*Reading the Weather*
Ed Catherall

Write **yes** or **no**.

Fill in your book file.

Bookfile
★ Fair
★★ Good
★★★ Excellent

# 11 Spell well

▶ Fill in the alphabet. Write capital letters for vowels and small letters for consonants.

| A | b | c | d | E | f | g | h | I | j | k | L | m | n | O | p | q | r | s | t | U | v | w | x | y | z |

As you work this page, use your dictionary to check your spellings.

▶ Read these words aloud and listen to the **two** vowels **ai** making **one** sound.

air — chair — fairy — stair

▶ Add more words to the string.

____ — fair — airy — hair

▶ Read these words aloud and listen to **ai** making a slightly different sound.

rain — brain — vain — obtain

▶ Add more words to the string.

____ — pain — plain — train

▶ Make a string of words for this **oa** sound.

oat — coat — boat — moat

____ — goat — soap

Find the **hidden word** in the spelling puzzle.

▶ Read the clues.

1. A farm animal with horns
2. Water falling in drops from the sky
3. We need this to be able to breathe
4. A word meaning important
5. A deep ditch round a castle
6. To point, throw or kick in a certain direction
7. A sudden attack

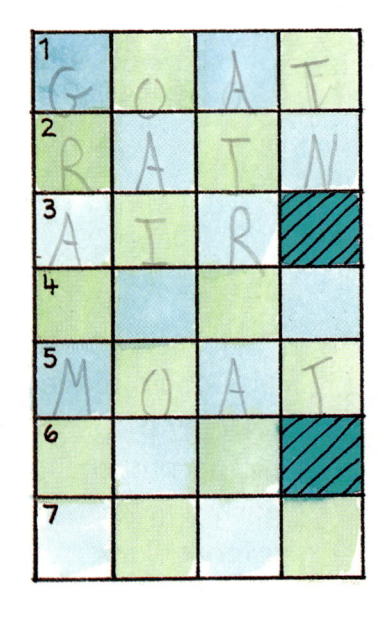

1. G O A T
2. R A I N
3. A I R
4. 
5. M O A T
6. 
7. 

▶ Write the hidden word going down from 1–7. _____

"Tell me some more 'tricky' words, Jan."

"Their and there sound the same."

"But they have different spellings and meanings."

---

**Dictionary**

their or theirs ... Belonging to them          there ... In that place

---

▶ Read this paragraph. Draw a line under the correct word from the brackets.

The (to <u>too</u> two) children went on a visit (<u>to</u> too two) London. (Their <u>There</u>) friend, Jan, went (<u>to</u> too two). They were met at the station by Lucy's grandparents, who took them all (<u>to</u> too two) Trafalgar Square (<u>to</u> too two) feed the pigeons. (There <u>Their</u>) they bought a bag (off <u>of</u>) corn (<u>to</u> too two) give (<u>to</u> too two) the pigeons. Unfortunately Lucy climbed onto one (<u>of</u> off) the statues and then fell (of <u>off</u>). 'I won't be taking you (their <u>there</u>) again, Lucy,' said her grandfather.

"Two spelling rules for plurals."

When a word ends with **ey ay** or **oy uy** add an **s**.

boys

When a word ends with a consonant, followed by a **y**, change the **y** to **i**, then add **-es**.

baby babies

One d**ay** ... two d**ays**     one bab**y** ... two bab**ies**

▶ Write the plurals of each of the following words.

key _keys_                fly _flies_              boy _boies_
play _plays plays_        journey _journeys_       lady _ladies_
story _stories_           cherry _cherries_        berry _berries_

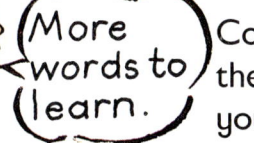

"More words to learn."

Copy each of these words into your notebook.

| does | pretty |
| people | yours |
| friend | could |

Practise each one. Cover each word over. Test yourself.

Notebook

▶ Play the **word growing** game with a friend, using 3 or 4 letter words. Take it in turns to begin a new word with the **second** letter of the previous word.

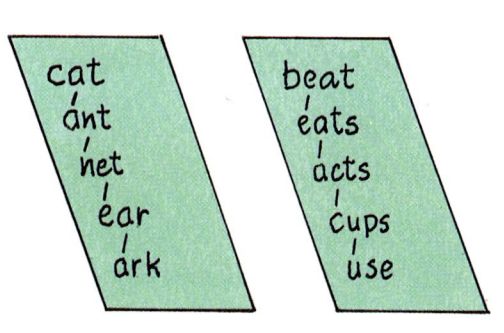

cat / ant / net / ear / ark

beat / eats / acts / cups / use

# 12 Which way next?

▶ Write the names of these places in on the map.

| 1 LIBRARY | 2 CHURCH | 3 POST OFFICE | 4 BANK |
| 5 SWEET SHOP | 6 CLEANERS | 7 NEWSAGENT | 8 HAIRDRESSERS |

▶ Draw a line like this . . . . . . . . . . to show the way from the LIBRARY in West Street to the HEALTH CENTRE in South Street.

Draw a line like this _ _ _ _ _ _ _ _ _ to show the way from the POST OFFICE on the corner of Chapel Street, to the BANK in the High Street.

Draw a line like this __ __ __ __ __ __ to show the way from the SWEET SHOP in East Street to the RESTAURANT on the corner of the High Street and West Street.

▶ Write **true** or **false** at the end of each sentence.

1 The supermarket is in the High Street. _____

2 The church is in Chapel Street by the car park. _____

3 Park Passage is between the library and the swimming baths. _____

4 The Town Hall is in East Street opposite a sweet shop. _____

5 There is a big block of offices in South Street. _____

6 The hairdressers and the cleaners are on the same side of the High Street. _____

▶ As you read this set of directions, follow the route on the map with your finger.

**From the Town Hall to the Health Centre**
    Cross the pedestrian crossing in East Street.
    Turn left on the corner into the High Street.
    Walk along the High Street to the corner of West Street.
    Walk along West Street and turn into South Street.
    Cross the pedestrian crossing to the Health Centre.

Is this the shortest way from the Town Hall to the Health Centre?

Write **yes** or **no**. ☐

▶ Write **directions** for the **shortest route** from the Town Hall to the Health Centre.

_____
_____
_____

You might see some of these pictograms in the High Street of any town.

*Pictograms are picture messages without words.*

Fill in your book file.

▶ Write in words what you think each one means.

1 _____  2 _____  3 _____

Book file
★ Fair
★★ Good
★★★ Excellent

# 13 Grammar

▶ Add 3 more nouns to each set.

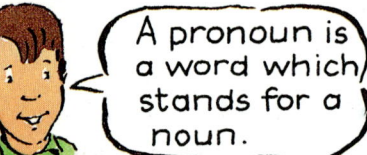

bird

Oxford

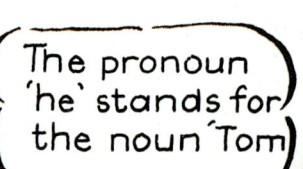

crowd

*A pronoun is a word which stands for a noun.*

*The pronoun 'he' stands for the noun 'Tom'.*

▶ Read these sentences.
Tom chose a nutty cake, but Tom didn't like it.
Tom chose a nutty cake, but **he** didn't like it.

▶ Read this list of pronouns.

| he | she |
| him | her |
| his | they |
| their | them |
| it | we |
| us | you |
| me | I |

▶ Read these sentences and draw a ring round all the **pronouns**.

1 When Mrs Piper turned the key, she found that it wouldn't open the door.
2 Mr Piper tried to kick a goal, but he fell flat on his face.
3 Jan told Tom that she would help him with his work if he gave her a ride on his new bicycle.
4 The children had no money for bus fares, so they decided to walk.
5 'If you give me some money,' said Tom hopefully, 'we can all have ice-creams.'

**Pronoun puzzle**

▶ Draw a ring round the hidden pronouns in these sentences.

1 Tom w(hi)stled a merry tune.

2 Lucy's father ran to catch the bus into Flitstone.

3 Jan found some white shells on Weston sands.

▶ Write the pronouns which you found here.

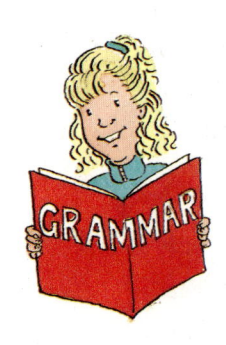

_____  _____  _____  _____

_____  _____  _____  _____

In this extract from a longer story, a creature called a Sea-Thing Child is hiding under a pile of stones on the sea-shore.

▶ As you read, notice that the pronoun **he** is used over and over again for the Sea-Thing Child.

All alone he was, and behind him the ocean roared and shook its fist. After a while, when the tide went out and the day grew warm, he crawled up the beach, leaving a wide and messy track behind him in the smooth sand. He went to the heaps of round sea-stones that ticked the ocean minutes rolling in the tide-wash when the tide was in. He sorted out the best round stones and broken bits of bottles, cups and saucers that the sea and sand had smoothed to sea-glass and sea-china. He ran back and forth between the heaps of round sea-stones and his place among the seaweed-bearded rocks, carrying sea-stones and sea-glass and sea-china. When he had enough he built a sea-stone igloo all around himself with no door and no window. When he was done he couldn't see a thing and he couldn't get out without taking it apart. So he sat there inside breathing hard and making faces!

▶ Count how many times the pronoun **he** is used for the Sea-Thing Child.

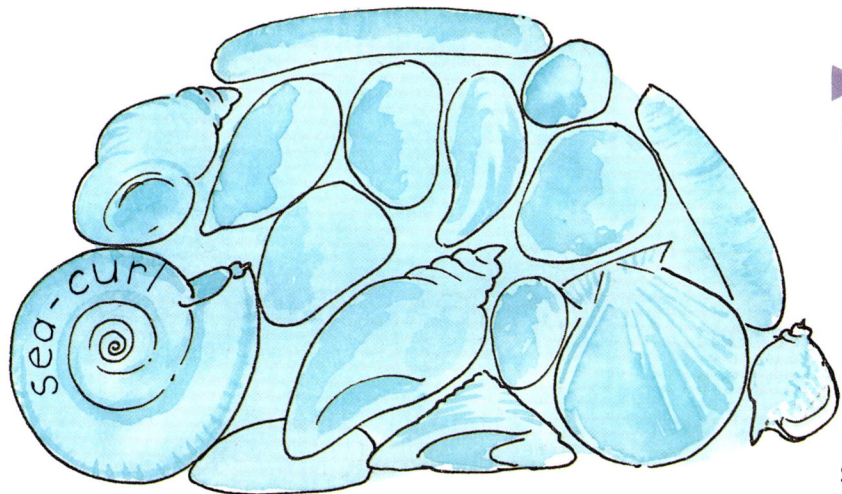

▶ Write a sea-sounding word in each of the stones in the igloo.

You can write real words like...
sea-shell and...
sea-fan...
and made up words like...
sea-saucer and...
sea-star.

▶ Read a little more of the story.

After a while the Sea-Thing Child heard a thin, whispering voice ... The voice sounded as if it had come from something small ... The Sea-Thing Child pushed some of the stones off the top of the igloo and stuck his head out ...

Now you have **two** imaginary creatures.
What do they look like? What will they say to each other?
Will they be friends or rivals?

Write about: **A Conversation between the Sea-Thing Child and ...**

# 14 The Thing

▶ Read this description.

Mr Willie Wonka was zooming through space in the Space Hotel.

Suddenly the door of one of the lifts began sliding slowly open and Mr Wonka could see that there was something . . . something thick . . . something brown . . . something with slimy skin and large eyes . . . squatting inside the lift.

Mr Willie Wonka was dumbstruck. He stood motionless, gaping at the thing in the lift, his mouth slightly open, his eyes stretched wide as two tanks.

It looked more than anything like an enormous egg balanced on its pointed end. It was as tall as a big boy and wider than the fattest man. The greenish-brown skin had a shiny wettish appearance and there were wrinkles in it. About three quarters of the way up there were two large, round eyes as big as tea-cups. The eyes were white, but each had a brilliant red pupil in the centre. The eyes were everything. There were no other features, no nose or mouth or ears, but the entire egg-shaped body was itself moving very very slightly, pulsing and bulging gently here and there as though the skin were filled with some thick fluid.

This description comes from **Charlie and the Great Glass Elevator** written by Roald Dahl.

Draw a picture in your notebook of **The Thing** from Roald Dahl's description.

▶ Complete these phrases about Mr Wonka as he stared at **The Thing**:

He was _____. He stood _____ . . .

his mouth _____, his eyes _____

_____.

▶ Write the adjectives which describe these nouns.

like an _____ egg     the _____ – _____ skin

a _____ _____ appearance     _____ , _____ eyes

_____ _____ pupils     _____ – _____ body

▶ Complete these comparisons.     Make up comparisons for:

it was as tall as a _____ _____     eyes as white as _____
eyes stretched wide as _____ _____     pupils as red as _____
     skin as wrinkled as _____

▶ Draw a line under the correct phrase from the description.

1 The Thing looked like
   . . . an enormous egg
   . . . a gigantic crab      balanced on
   . . . a monstrous dragon
   . . . a curled tail.
   . . . two long legs.
   . . . a pointed end.

2 The skin had
   . . . a polished, smooth
   . . . a shiny, wettish      appearance.
   . . . a rough, scaly

3 About
   . . . three quarters
   . . . half      of the way up
   . . . two thirds
   . . . were three narrow eye-slits.
   . . . was a blood-red eye.
   . . . were two large, round eyes.

4 The entire
   . . . egg-shaped
   . . . crab-shaped      body was moving very very slightly.
   . . . dragon-like

5 It seemed as though the skin were filled with
   . . . a kind of gluey liquid.
   . . . a poisonous gas.
   . . . some thick fluid.

▶ Now read each of the 5 sentences again, this time choosing phrases you **didn't** underline. Read the set of sentences over and over again to yourself.

Make a picture in your mind of another thing.
Imagine that you are seeing this thing.
Think about **where** you are when you see IT.

Write a description of: **IT**
You could make this description the beginning of a long story.

Fill in your book file.

Book file
★ Fair
★★ Good
★★★ Excellent

# 15 How in the world?

There are many different stories about how the world was made.

People of all races have tried to explain the great mystery by inventing their own creation **myths**.

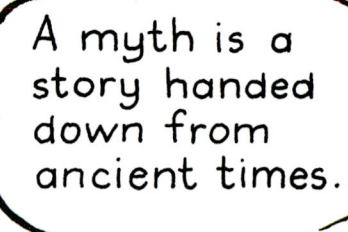

*A myth is a story handed down from ancient times.*

An Aboriginal myth from Australia tells how an Emu's egg was hurled into the sky. When the egg broke, the yolk became the bright, yellow sun.

A myth from India tells of a great, golden egg floating on the sea. After many ages, the egg broke open. One part became the sky and the other part became the earth.

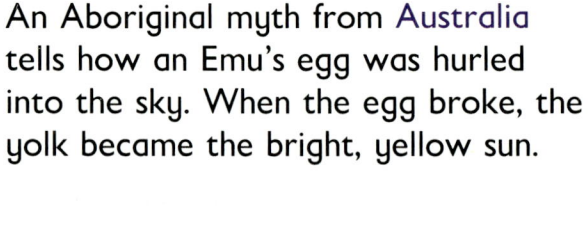

A creation myth from Ancient Greece tells how a beautiful dove laid an egg upon the waters of the world. When the egg hatched, out tumbled the sun, the moon and all the peoples of the world.

▶ Write here.

What is the **same** in all the myths? _____

Which idea do you like best?  Say why. _____

_____

Add more nouns which mean:
(a) story, (b) idea and (c) ancient
to your Thesaurus on pages 38–39.

▶ Read the beginning of this myth from China.

In the beginning the first man hatched from an egg. This man grew two metres a day until he became the great giant Pwanku. With only his tortoise for company, Pwanku pushed the Sky above the Earth. Then he set to work with his chisel and mallet to carve the mountains and valleys.

Is this paragraph mainly about:

how giants grow,
tortoises,
how a giant made the world?

▶ Draw a line under your answer.

▶ Read the next part of the story.

When Pwanku's work was done, he was so tired that he lay down and died. Now his great dead body was as useful as his living one had been. His voice became the thunder rolling among the mountains. His left eye became the light of the sun and his right eye became the light of the moon. His beard changed into stars, his skin and hair into grass and trees, while his breath became the clouds and winds. From his teeth and bones were formed the rocks and metals, whilst his sweat fell upon the earth as rain.

▶ Fill in the details.

After his work was over Pwanku's body was used like this:

His voice became _____

His left eye became _____

His right eye became _____

His breath became _____

How did the Chinese story say:

(a) the stars were made? _____
(b) the rocks and metals were made? _____
Where did the rain which fell upon the earth come from? _____
_____

# 16 On the air

Imagine that this book is being made into a story for **radio**.
What **sounds** might the producer use to set the scene, before the story begins?

*dog barking*
*horses' hooves   cows lowing*
*cock crowing*

**FARM HOLIDAY ADVENTURES**

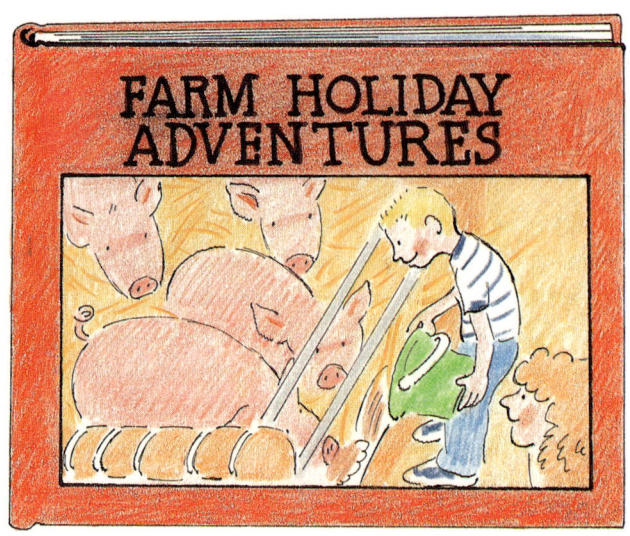

▶ Write a possible title for this book.

▶ Write the sounds which you might use to introduce the story and set the scene if you were the producer.

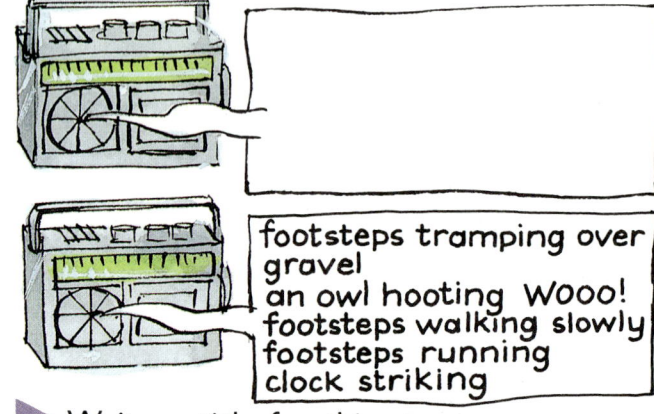

Think about stories which could follow on from each of these sets of sounds.

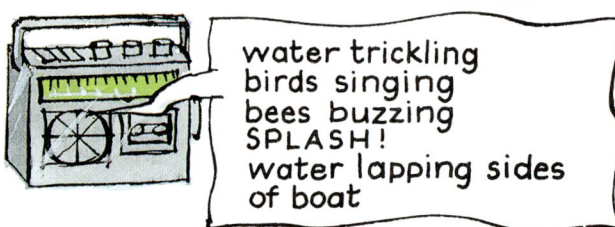

*water trickling*
*birds singing*
*bees buzzing*
*SPLASH!*
*water lapping sides of boat*

*footsteps tramping over gravel*
*an owl hooting Wooo!*
*footsteps walking slowly*
*footsteps running*
*clock striking*

▶ Write a title for this story.

▶ Write a title for this story.

▶ Read these titles for a radio programme.

　Boat Journey round Bird Island
　Disney Land
　Ghosts' Gallery

▶ Write the title of the programme you have chosen.

▶ Fill in your ideas for **sounds to introduce** one of the programmes.

▶ Read this story beginning.

'What's that noise?'
They all stood staring into the corner of the cupboard.
'Listen!'
It was very faint at first; tappings ... scratchings ... and a few feeble whimpers.
The children didn't move.
Gradually it grew louder – the tappings became rappings, the scratchings became scrabblings and the whimpers, no longer weak and far away, took on a low, throbbing sound.

▶ Write the words and phrases from the passage which describe sounds.

_____  _____  _____

_____  _____  _____

▶ Read this story beginning.

'All hands on deck!' It was the man on watch.
The sound of splitting timber was followed by a dull scrunch as the ship lurched over in the gale.
Above the roar of the wind and the shouts of the crew, came the desolate tolling of the ship's bell.
'Silence that bell!' roared a voice from the bridge.

▶ Write the phrases which describe the sounds.

_____  _____

_____  _____

Think about your radio story.

Read the 2 story beginnings and decide which one interests you most.

Write the sounds which you would use to set the scene for the story you have chosen.

Make notes for your story about:
1 **where** the story takes place,
2 **who** the people in the story are,
3 **what** happens **after** the story beginning.

Write: **A Radio Story**

Fill in your book file.

Book file
★ Fair
★★ Good
★★★ Excellent

# 17 In the papers

Do you remember **headlines**?
Headlines use small details to 'catch your eye'.
▶ Read these torn headlines.

FROZEN FURRY
BRRRRILLIANT!
FIREMAN FRANK
DANNY THE CHAMP
SWARMS OF BEES
ATTACK BABY IN BUGGY
QUEEN'S HORSE
RESCUES CHILDREN FROM B
GALLOPS BACK TO THE PAL
CITY TEAM
SAYS I'M THE GREATEST
WIN AFTER EXTRA TIME

▶ Write the 5 complete headlines.

_____
_____
_____
_____
_____

What else 'catches your eye' when you look in the papers?

Letters    Sports reports    Pictures of famous people    Star signs

Which would you read first?
▶ Make a list in order of your reading choice.

TV guide    Puzzles    Cartoons    Gardener's calendar    Advertisements    Competitions

▶ Read these 'Readers' letters'.

Dear Sir,
My canary, Joey, will be 21 years old on Friday. Is this a record?
Yours truly
A. Bird

Dear Sir or Madam,
Now I've seen everything! As I was walking down the High Street on Friday afternoon I saw a man wearing a snake round his neck instead of a scarf. Was he feeling the cold?
Yours faithfully
I. Tellem

Dear Sir or Madam
Have any of your readers got a dog like my Tip? When he wants to come in he jumps up at the door handle, holds it in his teeth till it turns, and lets himself in.
Yours faithfully
A. Mazed

You could make up a name for yourself.

▶ Write a short letter to **surprise** the readers.

▶ Read this cartoon.

**CHUCKLE WITH CHARLIE**
- Knock knock
- Who's there?
- Arthur.
- Arthur who?
- Arthur any cakes for tea today?

Notebook

Make up some more 'knock knock' jokes of your own.
You could try ... Ida ... for, 'I'd an idea ...'
　　　　　　　　Luke ... for, 'Look through the ...'
　　　　　　　　Howard ... for, 'How would ...?'

▶ Make your own joke into a cartoon.

# 18 Target

You will get to the **Target** if you can finish all the work on these two pages.

**1 ▶** Write each set of **nouns** in **alphabetical order**.

| Common nouns | Proper nouns | Collective nouns |
|---|---|---|
| guide _____ | Austria _____ | choir _____ |
| gutter _____ | Asia _____ | crowd _____ |
| gum _____ | Africa _____ | company _____ |
| guess _____ | Arctic _____ | crew _____ |
| guard _____ | America _____ | cluster _____ |

◎ ▶ Colour in ring 1 on the board.

**2 ▶** Make an **adjective** from each of these nouns.

sun _____    fog _____    mist _____
hair _____    dust _____    crust _____

◎ ▶ Colour in ring 2 on the board.

**3 ▶** Write the **pronoun** in the box at the end of the sentence.

1 Tom's father gave him a £5 note.
2 Lucy picked up the wrapper and put it in the bin.
3 Jan's grandma took her to the Zoo.
4 Both children had lost their pencils.
5 'We will go home now,' said Mr and Mrs Lock.

◎ ▶ Colour in ring 3 on the board.

**4 ▶** Make **opposites** by writing **un-** or **dis-** in front of the following verbs.

____ tie   ____ appear   ____ agree   ____ do   ____ believe

Use each **verb** in a sentence of your own.

1 _____
2 _____
3 _____
4 _____
5 _____

◎ ▶ Colour in ring 4 on the board.

## 5 ▸ Write **true** or **false** at the end of each sentence.

1 To 'turn over a new leaf' means to make a fresh start.
2 Another word for ridiculous is sensible.
3 Impudent means rude.
4 A verb is a describing word.
5 Another word for enemy is foe.
6 The plural of fly is flyes.
7 A jungle is a thick forest.
8 Words actually spoken are written inside inverted commas.
9 A pronoun is a word which stands for a noun.
10 The letter Q is always followed by the letter Y.

◉ ▸ Colour in ring 5 on the board.

## 6 ▸ Complete each of these **comparisons**.

1 as _____ as snow

2 as _____ as grass

3 as _____ as night

4 as quick as _____

5 as slow as _____

6 as cunning as _____

◉ ▸ Colour in ring 6 on the board.

## 7 ▸ Write 2 words which have **similar** meanings for each of these words.

excellent
_____
_____

ridiculous
_____
_____

crowd
_____
_____

said
_____
_____

quiet
_____
_____

noisy
_____
_____

▸ Colour in ring 7 on the board.

Did you get to the Target?
Write **yes** or **no**.

# 19 Your Thesaurus

Nouns  Verbs  Adjectives

ancient

to ask

to begin

quiet

excellent

very good
super
astounding
fantastic
fabulouse

big

clue

**fault** — Defect, Blemish, failing, mistake, slip, weakness

**idea**

**noisy**

**to see**

**to run**

**small**

**story**

**ridiculous** — crazy, daft, stupid, silly, nuts, bonkers, zany

## 20 Book file

This is your **personal record** of the books you are **reading**.

▶ Write the **title** of each book and the name of the **author**.
Give each book a star rating like this: * Fair    ** Good    *** Excellent

| Title | Author | Star rating |
|---|---|---|
|  |  |  |
|  |  |  |
|  |  |  |
|  |  |  |
|  |  |  |
|  |  |  |
|  |  |  |

▶ Think again about all the books in your book file.
Which **one** did you enjoy most? Say **why**.
_____
_____

Which **one** did you like least? Say **why**.
_____
_____